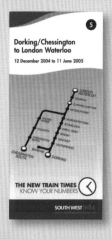

Timepiece

Designing modern time

21
20
19
18
LOND
8273

Timepiece
Designing modern time

David Lawrence   *with a foreword by David Rooney*

Published to accompany Network Rail's *A New Timepiece for the Railway* design competition managed by the Royal Institute of British Architects.

First published in the UK in 2023 by Between Books
Essay and edit © 2023 David Lawrence
Foreword © 2023 David Rooney

Copyright in the images remains with the creators or owners of the images as listed in the Image Credits

ISBN 978-0-9536980-7-3

Design: Guy Eaglesfield
Typeface: Rail Alphabet 2
Editor and production manager: David Lawrence

Printed and bound in England by The Aldgate Press 2023

Contents

Foreword

The story of time is the story of us. For thousands of years, we have used time and clocks – broadly defined – to make sense of our world, to create order, and to control the myriad activities of everyday life. Clocks have in many ways become our avatars: we express our own identities with and through clocks, particularly those in prominent public view. In this thoughtful and absorbing volume, David Lawrence offers an insightful vision of the significance of clocks and time in the railway story and, more broadly, to modern culture.

A crucial aspect of modernity is standardisation. Standard time – adopting a single time across a wide geographical area rather than keeping local times – began with the early railways. Where would we be without standard time today? It is the operating system for the infrastructure of the modern world: not just transport networks but telecommunications, information technologies, global finance, logistics, power distribution, water supply, surveying, meteorology – the list is extensive. Without standard time – which began as railway time – our world would simply shut down.

Yet this is a much wider story than technology. As David demonstrates here, the rail network is, in itself, a temporal performance: it is a clock. The railway comprises a set of human and non-human actors performing together in an exquisitely complex choreography in time as well as space – its daily operation marks the passage of time as surely as do the clocks in the stations, control rooms, signal boxes and platforms within it. Our experience of time when travelling by rail is, as David points out, uniquely human. The clocks around the network give us the beat. They are the metronomes of modernity.

Of course, most of us carry our own personal timekeepers these days, and it would be possible to conclude that these smartphones and wristwatches are sufficient to navigate our railway journeys successfully. But railway clocks are different. Or rather, they perform an important task in addition to giving us the time of day. Like the railways themselves, public clocks connect us with each other, and with ourselves, in complex and profound ways stretching back millennia. In today's fraught and fragmenting world, these connections have never been needed more.

David Rooney
Author of *About Time: A History of Civilization in Twelve Clocks*

Timepiece, and piece of time

Waterloo Station by Terence Cuneo, 1967.

Time organises everything we do. Time meters our sleeping, working, resting, study, leisure, industry, meeting, celebration, meditation, worship, and travel; it measures our birth, life, and death; it regulates simple actions and complex processes; it calibrates our heartbeat. Time is communicated through timekeeping and time outputting devices, which we call clocks and watches: timepieces.[1]

This book tells you about railway time and railway timekeepers. It describes the history and design of the railway clock. Without time railways cannot function, because railways exist to sell safe travel and this requires precise, standardised time. Railway time is consistent, reliable, uniform. It drives the passenger announcements, the flows of trains, and is visible throughout the travel spaces where people and movement come together. Railway time assures passengers of safe travel. It makes the signals work, the tickets valid, the trains and people move. One standard time is essential for travellers and operators to know when to expect the train to arrive and depart, and how long to wait for the next service. One standard time makes the journey happen. That's why we need clocks: to communicate the same time everywhere on the network.

Railways are businesses and social networks. Train time information is third of thirty-four factors which make stations work well for passengers, rated above shops, security, staff, toilets, reliability of services, and speed of journey. Railways generate revenue by selling safe travel. Trains connect people, industry, markets, customers. Time is travel, and time is money. The railway network is a fixed web of rails which carry the trains. Railway time is the disciplined and synchronised measurement of objects moving in spaces.[2] For example, you travel to the station: that takes a number of hours, minutes, seconds. Your train travels from station to station: that movement is also measured in time. The only difference here is speed: the different speeds of you and the train moving through spaces change the duration of time needed for the journey. The clock confirms to us where we need to be in relation to the train. If we are early, we can do other things; if we are 'on time' we join the train; if we are late, we can only run. In the timetable-train-clock-decision-action sequence, the railway clock is essential to railway operators, and to us.

Railway time makes a special kind of space. Railway stations represent one of the largest estates of public-private space in Britain, as important as airports and with similar captive audiences who wait, meet, and shop. Historically, railway stations have not always been considered as venues for good design, but railway time, space, and place are central to culture. Through this book we make a *journey to and through the station*, explaining where and why we encounter timepieces in the railway environment. Notes about the design and use of railway timepieces are included on pages in highlight boxes. This also explores the anatomy of the clock and shows some of the technology behind the clock face. It gives a survey of the best railway clocks around the world and includes a selection of international transport clocks which feature good design.

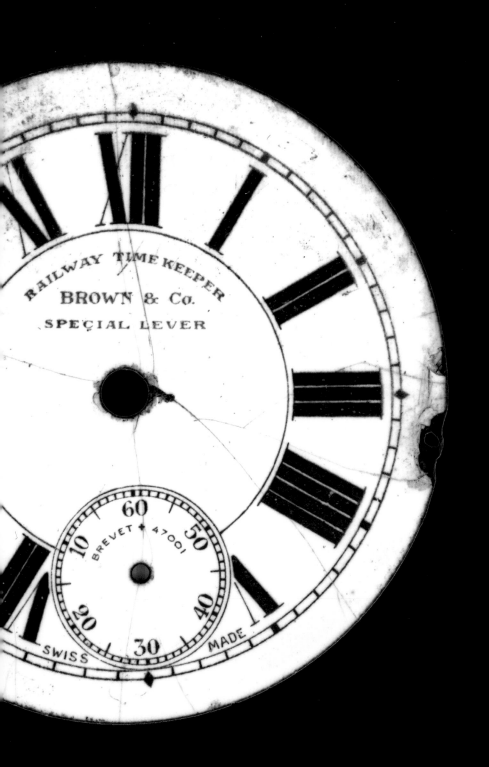

In fact, time does not exist. Yes, the universe is in motion: this is studied through astrophysics. True, the universe and everything in it, including us, has beginnings, periods of growth, change, decay, and endings. True too that biology has an inbuilt timekeeper: we see that in the durations of organisms' lives from the fruit fly to trees and bacteria, and in circadian rhythms; but only humans have this system of measurement we call time. Clocks, on the railway and carried by us on wrist or phone, don't have a memory. For a timekeeping/time-outputting device it is always *now*, in a continuous flow and stream of moments and numbers. Only we experience time as a duration, a sense of flow and pause and interruption. Time is our perception of being in relation to the things around us: physics and our senses working together. For us, time is the meticulous certainty of a life frozen in Dutch and Spanish *vanitas* paintings, *and* the span and blur of a story. It is the length of the multitude of movements and moments in a sports match or a game, or a meeting, or a meal. Time is the space of a download, upload, and transfer indicated by Apple Mac 'spinning wait cursor', the Microsoft Windows 'wait cursor', and a multitude of 'throbber' loading icons.

Railway time is the place where we are geographically. Our space during the journey is a place too, moving through time. It is 'here' to 'there': railway time-travel brings 'here' closer to 'there'. With speed, places gain proximity, seem to merge, so that villages become suburbs, and suburbs city quarters. With time before our train, we find a freedom impossible anywhere else in life. A journey to a loved one can be too, too, slow; a journey to work much too fast, unless we are late. The flow of time is called *chronos*. Without time, we are without hope. With time, we can move. There is a right or opportune time for acting: this is *kairos*. Time is a commodity and a currency. It is lost and found. We can save it, spend it, keep it, waste it, kill it, have too much of it, use it, mark it, beat it, be ahead of it or behind it. We're in it or out of it; it's fast or slow, and it passes. Time can be long or short, a fleeting moment or an interminable delay. Timelessness takes us backwards and forwards beyond measured time. Our present is always becoming our past, and the future is instantly with us. That is why a long train journey with a film or book, or friend seems to be quicker than a shorter journey with nothing to entertain us.

Railway time is music and movies, where the speed of

successive moments fools our brains into seeing and hearing flow. Time is the pace and pauses of songs and poetry: the looping rhythms of Jimmy Forrest's *Night Train* performed by James Brown, and the electronic pulses of Giorgio Moroder's theme to the film *Midnight Express*; the wheel-on-rail percussion in W. H. Auden's poem *Night Mail* (written for a documentary film about postal mail carried by train), the stopped and listening stillness of a train in Edward Thomas's *Adlestrop*, the dream-drift journey in Sylvia Plath's *Getting There*.

The railway environment is a theatre where workers and travellers perform activities. Some activities are conditioned by time – the formal organisation of the railway. Others are just in time, or out of time: lovers kiss in *Brief Encounter*; a pop group escapes their fans in *A Hard Day's Night* and a secret agent investigates crime, both at Marylebone; one man pursues a *Mission: Impossible* at Liverpool Street; another escapes pursuers at Grand Central Terminal in *North by Northwest*; and yet another fails to make a meeting in *The Third Man*; dance brings stations to vivid life in *The Fisher King* and *Slumdog Millionaire*. And time is waiting in the threshold between one move and another: this is lost time and found time. That is railway time, station time, train time: time travel.

This book also considers the future design of the railway clock. The Network Rail system has 2,563 stations. Of these, 298 are category 'D' medium staffed stations, 679 are category 'E' small, staffed stations, and 1,200 are category 'F' small unstaffed stations. Displays showing the time are important at these locations where other facilities may be more limited. We have clocks in our mobile devices. We still wear wristwatches for their usefulness and beauty. What is the point and purpose of the railway clock now? Looking at the history of railway clocks, and at exemplary clock and watch design, what could be the form, appearance, size, materials, colours, and mechanisms of a new standard clock face for Britain's railways now, and into the future?

Time to unwind.

INTERCITY

Poster for British Rail *Intercity* services, published January 1990. An award-winning television advertisement featuring an animated version of this image had been created by agency Saatchi & Saatchi in 1989.

About clocks and control

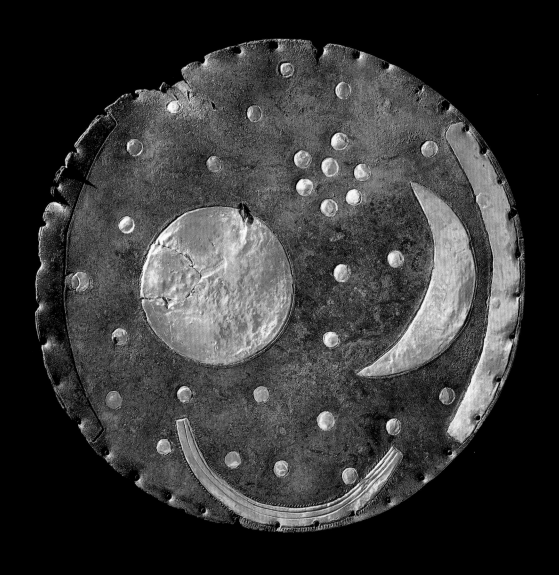

The need to measure and fix time emerged early in recorded human history, related to gaining better methods of predicting the position and alignment of Sun, Moon, and other planets and stars for the purposes of prediction and ritual, and for structuring events including regular worship and legal proceedings.

Clocks are used for quantifying periods shorter than a day. 'Telling the time' means counting and displaying numerical information, the counting of equal units used to subdivide each one Earth revolution around the Sun into hours, minutes, and seconds. The clock, whatever its system of analogue and digital operation, is simply a device for displaying and communicating the number of units counted at any point in the day-night cycle.

The Babylonians (first millennium BC) divided the circle into 360 parts and measured their years in twelve sections of 30 days each, creating the geometrical basis for measuring time in hours and minutes.

The clock face is a dial or map of the day, and we can find dials with markers created to identify a time or times of day beginning to be developed in many cultures from around 3100 BC. By 1500 BC the people of Egypt had made large sundials - or 'shadow clocks' - in the landscape; these were reduced in size by later peoples to produce a variety of time-telling devices.

Early time measurement devices dated to the second millennium BC comprised vessels containing sand or water which passed through an aperture at a controlled rate. When the sand or water had passed entirely through the aperture, a measured duration had elapsed. In the second century BC water clocks were linked by geared wheels to graduated scales with indicators. Romans called the water clock *horologium*, this name subsequently forming

Above: *Klepsydrae*, or water clocks.

Opposite: The *Nebra Sky Disc*, the world's oldest known representation of astronomical phenomena. From the Disc we discover something of how the world and the heavens were perceived in the second to first millennium BC.

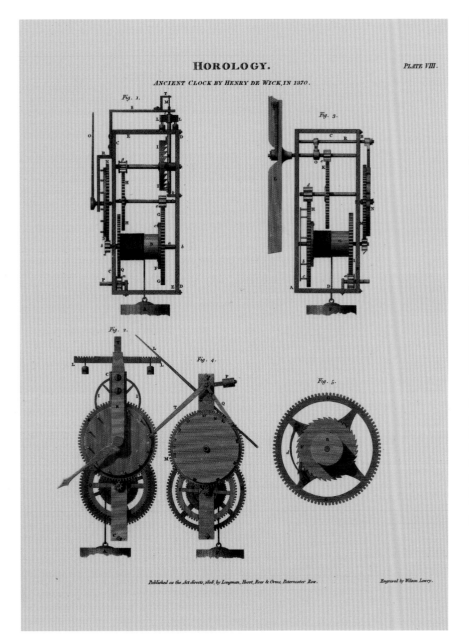

HOROLOGY.

ANCIENT CLOCK BY HENRY DE WICK, IN 1370.

PLATE VIII.

Fig. 1.

Fig. 2.

Fig. 3.

Fig. 4.

Fig. 5.

Published as the Act directs, 1808, by Longman, Hurst, Rees & Orme, Paternoster Row.

Engraved by Wilson Lowry.

Left and above: Timekeeping machines are groups of toothed wheels and pinions arranged together to divide stored power into equal units we call *hours* and *minutes*. Early clock works counted these units and caused bells to strike at certain intervals. Additional mechanisms enabled the power to be 'taken off' to drive a 'hand' or 'hands' around a dial to give a visual indication of the units counted – which we call *time*.

the basis of words used in many languages for mechanical clocks. Greeks used the name *klepsydra*. Even in the seventeenth century, these hourglasses and water clocks were in use by some cultures.

Mechanical clocks are an assembly of wheels – the *clockwork* – connected to a source of energy, typically a weight, spring, or since the early nineteenth century, an electrical impulse. The energy causes the wheels to turn. As each wheel is shaped to engage with adjacent wheels through its 'teeth', and the number of 'teeth' is calculated in precise ratios to divide and multiply, intervals of duration can be counted. One wheel driving the hand showing hours makes a complete revolution in twelve hours; another moves sixty times faster, to actuate the minute hand. Connected wheels and pinions are called *trains*. Without regulation the clock would be inaccurate, so designers invented mechanisms called escapements whose apparent delicacy controls the powerful movement of the other wheels. It is the escapement which 'tic-tacs' or 'tick-tocks'.

Early mechanical clocks (developed from about 1330) had no dials or 'faces'; they were large machines which marked divisions of the day and night by the periodic striking of a bell or bells. These machines had the name *clocca*. Later in the fourteenth century the clock mechanism was reduced in size to be used in domestic settings.

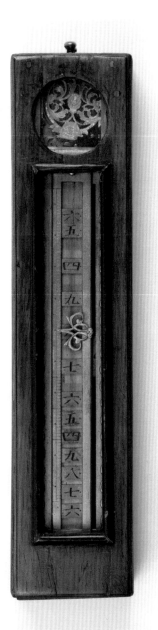

Right: Pillar clock (Shaku Tokei), Japan, 19th century.

Measurement of time has not always been standard throughout the world. In Japan before 1870 the equal division of days and relatively shorter nights produced different lengths of hour in the day or night and in the different seasons, called temporal hours.

When dials were introduced to give a visual display of the time, only one hand was fitted, and this pointed to the hour. Jost Bürgi invented the minute hand in the early 1580s. Galileo Galilei had first proposed the pendulum as an oscillator with its own natural frequency; Christiaan Huygens added this to clock mechanisms in 1656. By the fifteenth century additional dials could be included in clock faces to indicate seconds, the phases of the moon, the day and date, or the position of the stars for astronomical and astrological purposes. In addition to showing the time, water and mechanical clocks could be arranged to operate automata or other objects apparently moving without human intervention.

Opposite: Prague astronomical clock installed about 1486.

Time is our attempt to order the movement of objects in space, beginning with the solar system: the transit of the rotating Earth around the Sun (a year) and the transit of the Moon around the Earth (a month).

Right: Fourteenth century clock, Wells Cathedral, Somerset.

The exterior face incorporates automata which strike bells above the dial.

Watch with calendar,
around 1800.

Pocket watch, Philipp Matthäus Hahn,
Echterdingen, around 1785.

Pocket watch, Switzerland, around 1850.

Clock and watch technology continued to develop. The achievement of accurate longitudinal navigation at sea is due to special kinds of clock and watch called *chronometers*; these could also be used for precision timing of events.

By the mid-eighteenth century the production of time - through time-telling equipment - was itself industrialised and has benefitted from continuous innovation ever since. Clocks would become one of the first ubiquitous machines: cheap, reliable, and inspiring confidence. The dial clock – typically with a round 'face', but sometimes square or rectangular – was a visible and legible regulator of people. Timekeepers became invaluable throughout many cultures: first for industrial efficiency, secondly for status, and then for corporate and individual participation in the modern world to co-operate with industry and its associated effects. Time measurement also made efficient communication possible.

Cuckoo clockwork, Black Forest, around 1870.

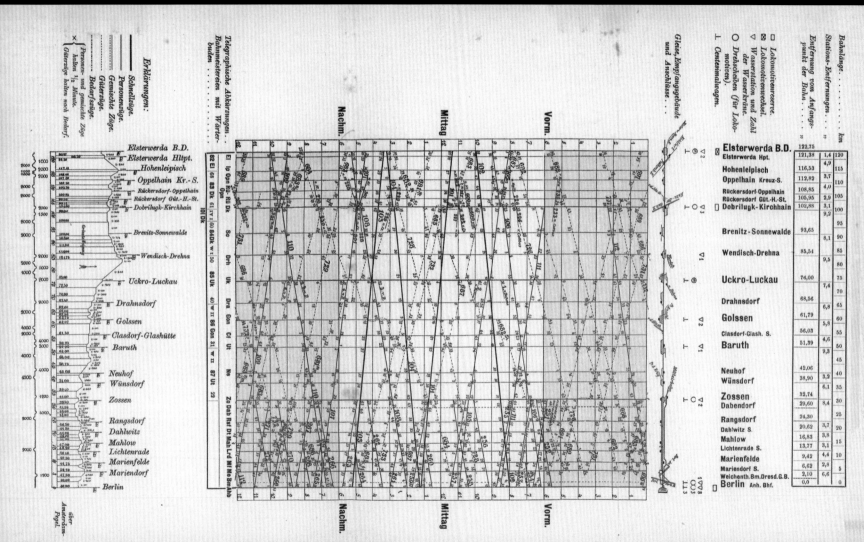

Above: A Cartesian diagram of train movements.

Stations are arranged on the vertical axis, and may be spaced proportionally to the distance between each stop. The horizontal axis is marked in regular divisions of time. The speed and distance are indicated by the angle of the lines representing trains.

Opposite: A graphical timetable used to represent sequential train movements coordinated by time and distance.

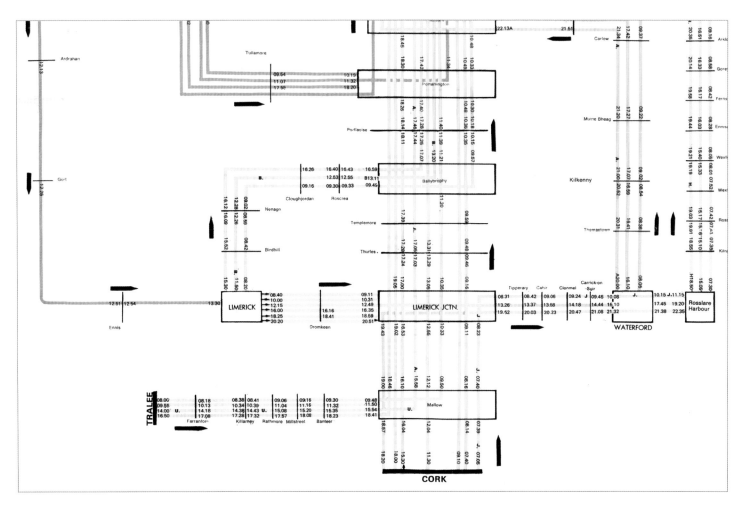

Wherever it is found, railway time brings order to the complexity and apparent disorder of transport activities. It is modernity regulated by machines. With increasing industrialisation and trading over distances, railways defined punctuality.

To operate railway networks, trains must be allowed to move as quickly and directly as possible. A very early requirement for timekeeping on railway networks was to ensure trains moved along routes at a safe distance from other trains. At first, elapses of time were considered sufficient to allow the train to have travelled from one point to another were estimated from the train's speed over the distance traversed, because there was no technology to confirm or communicate the train's position.

For LOCAL TRAINS and INTERMEDIATE STATIONS between WATERLOO and SURBITON and COMPLETE SERVICE between WATERLOO and GUILDFORD, see pages 394 to 426.

LONDON, GODALMING, HASLEMERE, PETERSFIELD PORTSMOUTH, and THE ISLE OF WIGHT

Down — Saturdays excepted

Stations (with distances in miles): WATERLOO dep., Surbiton, Esher, for Sandown Park, Hersham, Walton-on-Thames, Weybridge A, West Weybridge, Byfleet B, Woking C, Worplesdon, Guildford arr./dep., Farncombe, Godalming, Milford, Witley, Haslemere, for Hindhead, Liphook, Liss, Petersfield, Rowlands Castle, Havant, Hayling Island arr., Bedhampton Halt, Hilsea Halt, Fratton, Portsmouth & Southsea, Portsmouth Harbour arr., Ryde Pier Head, Esplanade, St. John's Road, Ashey, Haven Street, Wootton, Whippingham, Newport arr./dep., Carisbrooke Halt, Calbourne & Shalfleet, Ningwood, Yarmouth, Freshwater arr., Mill Hill, Cowes arr., Brading, St Helens, Bembridge arr., Sandown, Shanklin, Wroxall, Ventnor arr.

Conveyance of Motor Cars, etc., to and from the Isle of Wight, see pages 499 and 500

For Saturday Trains, see pages 361 to 363. For SUNDAY TRAINS, see pages 364 to 365. For Notes, see page 365.

Left: From Cartesian diagrams and graphical timetables, schedules of train times are arranged in clearer formats.

Above: In south-west England, the dial on Bristol's Corn Exchange has an additional minute hand installed between 1840 and 1852 when standard time was still a novelty in the city. The additional hand indicates 'railway' or London time which is ten minutes later.

Railways used clocks from the late 1830s, when the first long-distance routes were opened. Standard, or 'Greenwich' or 'London' time reached most of Great Britain with the railways from 1852, although this was sometimes regarded as an imposition on 'local' or 'town' time until legislation addressed the potentially confusing and expensive discrepancy. All parts of Britain were required to standardise clocks to display Greenwich mean time as a result of the Statutes (Definition of time) Act, 1880.[3] Local time was erased, solar time rejected.

Before railway operators used electrical systems for distributing one standard time across the network, it was the work of the train guard or conductor to correct their clock at the main departure station, and then to communicate the time from their clock to each station along a route. In this way time was quite literally *carried* across the country until 1939. Telegraphy and telephones were soon used to share a common understanding of the

Left: In the semi-automation of train signalling, developed in Britain after 1945, time and technology came together in special control centres. This is Hyndland, north-west of Glasgow, 1960.

Above: Whilst British railways operated to a single standard time from 1880, railways in North America pass through four time zones.

time, transmitted from London by morse code and other special bell codes every day until 1975.

Many mechanical and electrical signalling-related devices were invented to improve safety. The signalling systems used today are based on the same principle of maintaining an interval between different trains to avoid conflicting movements or accidents. Every movement is part of a sequence of movements, regulated so that there are no conflicts in the movements. Each movement has a

fixed and unique timing, planned graphically on Cartesian diagrams and graphical timetables of trains moving in space, through time. The diagrams are documented in printed and online tables which associate the arrival and departure times of individual trains with stations served by the trains.

SHEERWATER   BYFLEET   BYFLEET GRID   WEYBRIDGE

NEW HAW

Opposite: Panel, traction electricity supply control room, Woking, Surrey, 2020.

To and through the station, finding the time

36

This page: The turret clock of King's Cross Station, London. This three-dial machine set in the brick Italianate tower of architect Lewis Cubitt's building, has indicated the time to travellers and Londoners since 1852.

Opposite left: Brighton Station, England. Opened 1840–41 and designed in the office of David Mocatta, the station façade features a clock dial surrounded by ornate neo-classical decoration.

Opposite right: Portsmouth and Southsea Station, England, clock of 1876.

Streets and spaces around the station in city or town are full of sense stimulation; shops and cafes compete with advertising for our attention. In more remote places, we may be looking for a reassuring source of information about trains and service times. In this section we will consider a selection of historic station environments to note actual locations of time-telling equipment. We also look at the recent designs for Network Rail modular stations where there are many possibilities for the provision of clocks.

Railways contributed to the maintenance of national time, by installing many thousands of clocks at stations, on trains, in the multitude of private offices and public spaces, workshops and depots of the railway network. Many railway stations built between the mid-1800s and late 1900s have featured clocks prominently as part of the architectural design.

By the mid-1960s the British railway operator owned around 57,000 timepieces. Many of these durable and reliable devices functioned effectively for over an century. Everyone operating the network needed access to a timekeeper, and everyone using the network wanted to be reassured that and reminded that their transport links were available and operational… and 'on' time.

Railways could produce vehicles in their own workshops, and build stations and tracks to their own designs, but clocks, like telephones and signalling equipment, required a higher level of precision and a cleaner manufacturing environment.

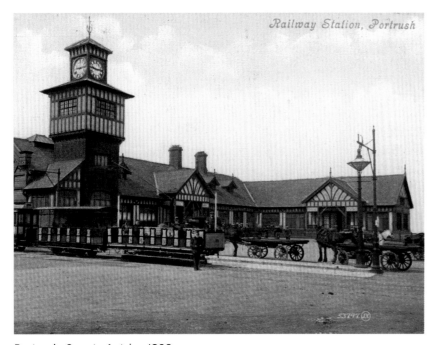

Portrush, County Antrim, 1893.

Stirling, Scotland, 1916.

Of over four hundred specialist clock and watch makers in England, Scotland, Wales, France, Germany, Japan, Switzerland, and the United States of America, notable manufacturers are Thomas Armstrong & Brother (Manchester), William Avison (York), Ball (Leicester), Dent (London), Gent (Leicester), J.B. Joyce (Whitchurch), John Smith (Derby), William Potts (Leeds), Thwaites & Reed (London), John Walker (London).

Clockmakers preferred to offer a range of their own designs suited to their technology, knowing that the railways must choose from the range available. 'Special railway timekeepers' were made as pocket watches.

Larger clocks displayed on or near station exteriors followed the practice of architectural and horological developments: dials on free-standing stone features (clock towers); dials on small towers fixed to buildings or built into walls ('turret' clocks). In these settings the clock provides a visual focus amongst the architectural details; it will be a prominent feature as a public display of railway time, and in the better examples the building designers have used the form of the dial to balance the other features of the tower or facade.

Considering Britain and Ireland, important examples of public railway clocks are found at Bristol Temple Meads, Carlisle Citadel, Charing Cross (London); Cleethorpes, Dublin Connolly, Eastbourne, Glasgow Central, Holyhead, Kings Cross (London), Newcastle Central, Nottingham (now part of the Victoria Shopping Centre), Portrush (Berkeley

Gare Limoges-Bénédictins, France, 1927–9.

Paris Gare de Lyon, France, 1899.

Deane Wise, 1893), St Pancras, London (George Gilbert Scott, 1868–76), Scarborough (G T Andrews, 1845/1882), Waterloo (London), Wemyss Bay, Whitley Bay, and York.

In Europe and North America, many clocktowers and station clocks based on classical architectural styles are found. Selected examples are Limoges-Bénédictins, France (Roger Gonthier, 1927–9), Paris Gare de Lyon, France (Marius Toudoire, 1899), the former Paris Gare d'Orsay (Victor Laloux, Lucien Magne and Émile Bénard, 1900), Stockholm (Adolf Wilhelm Edelsvärd, 1867–71), and Waterbury, Connecticut (McKim, Mead and White, about 1909).

Stations built from the 1830s to the 1930s present a wide variety of styles and standards of design. Many of them constructed using stone, or brick, or steel and concrete were made to present an image of a safe and reliable train operator. Using classical styles of architecture, featuring perhaps towers or pediments, station architects would frequently integrate dial clocks into the main road-facing side of the building, slipped into classical roundels perhaps, or embellished with swags of laurels or fruit.

Cleethorpes, England, 1884.

Holyhead, Isle of Anglesey, 1878–80.

Opposite: Railway time is public time too. The Gothic clocktower of Bristol Temple Meads, England, 1878, by Matthew Digby Wyatt.

Railway Station, Temple Meads, Bristol.

41

REFRESHMENT ROOMS

BOVRIL

RUGBY

REFRESHMENT ROOM SECOND CLASS

JOYCE
WHITCHURCH

NEXT TRAIN WILL DEPART AT

NEXT TRAIN WILL DEPART AT

EUSTON ONLY.

WILLESDEN, BRIGHTON & EASTBOURNE

TELEGRAPH OFFICE
BOOKING OFFICE
GENTLEMEN
CLOAK ROOM
WAY OUT

L. & N.W. Station, Rugby. Southern Platform.

Greers Series. 68

Andover, England (**above**) and Perth, Scotland (**right**).

Inside railway stations clocks have been provided in the ticket hall and waiting area(s), on the platforms used by passengers, and in the railway operator's private spaces. Clocks in public and industrial situations were mounted to be visible and keep the ground free of obstructions. Dials were suspended from roofs or mounted on decorative brackets (dial, multi-dial and platform clocks and 'mural' clocks); dials in metal or wood cases projected from walls; cabinets contained a dial (wall-hanging or floor-standing 'drop-case', 'long case' or 'trunk' clocks and 'bracket' clocks); smaller timepieces were placed on interior fittings and furniture ('mantel' and 'desk' clocks).

If a clock was in a location where it could not easily be seen from a distance, it could project at right angles from the façade on metal brackets laced together with arabesques and scrolls. This is the old Euston Station, London, 1962.

Brighton, England, 1841.

Glasgow Central, Scotland, rebuilt 1901–5.

Paddington, over the loggia or 'Clock Arch' forming the original main entrance to the station. Installed around 1854 and restored 1985, this was the largest triple-dial clock in Britain.

Since 2007 London St Pancras has been the English terminal of the *Eurostar* rail link to continental Europe. St Pancras has been rebuilt and restored by London & Continental Railways as a multi-level station, shopping centre, and hotel. The 5.15 metre-diameter timepiece on the southern screen of the trainshed has its own interesting history.

Accounts vary, but it is known that railway employee Roland Hoggard purchased the original clock when it was extensively damaged during removal between 1961 and 1968. Hoggard fashioned a reconstruction of the clock on the wall of a building in Nottinghamshire. This was copied by Dent & Co. to make a new clock for St Pancras. After Roland Hoggard died in 2013 the remains of the original timepiece were moved to the Museum of Timekeeping at the British Horological Institute.

Clock cases unite fine cabinet making in a selection of exotic and durable timbers, with precise work in metal and glass. Larger suspended or bracketmounted timepieces may feature single or multiple dials. The dials are frequently of opal or white glass. Numerals and hands are painted or printed. Dials may be illuminated by an interior light source or external spotlights. Triangular spaces between dial and cabinet invite complex decoration in carved or cast and painted metal and timber. A polished metal bezel – or in the smaller clocks a moulded timber bezel – retains a glass window over the dial and hands, within the moulded surround. Hands are 'blued', a finish effected by heating the steel to a certain temperature. **Clockwise from left**: York, England; Dalmally, Scotland; Stalybridge, England (replica of original); York, England.

Working round the Region

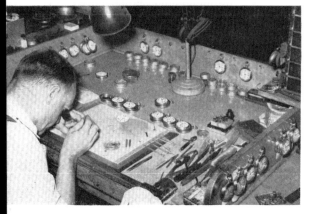

Above: Arthur Taylor delicately replaces the balance staff of a watch.

Below: Reg Wrigley's machine cleans a watch in seven minutes.

Clock and Watch Repair Shop, Manchester

Above: Wilf Pilling at work on a double-dialled clock.

Below: Sid Bird carefully replaces the many parts.

SITUATED IN Osborne Street, Manchester, the Clock and Watch Repair Shop is under the control of J. Cunningham, who is responsible to the Supplies & Contracts Manager.

The shop was brought into being in 1894 by the former L & Y railway and although the present staff only consists of Supervisor, Chargehand, four instrument repairers and a stores issuer, the volume of work turned out today is many times greater than would have been thought possible at that time.

All the goods and passenger guards' watches on the L M R are repaired here – together with the watches of the Scottish Region – and the whole of our Region's wall and mantel clocks with the exception of those from the London area. In addition, repairs are carried out on such varied instruments as time recording machines, watchman's patrol clocks, ship's clocks, stop watches and all the outside stations' clocks in the Northern area.

The number of repairs carried out at Osborne Street during the last year amounted to 7,321 watches, 1,219 portable clocks and 219 fixed clocks. To enable this kind of work to be undertaken no less than 125 different spare parts are stocked, some hardly visible to the naked eye.

One who has seen many changes in clock design is the Supervisor, Harold West. Having served more than 35 years at Osborne Street, Harold remembers when they had many varied types of timepieces and also used to repair ticket issuing machines. Proof of his skill was shown when he, along with one of his colleagues, Wilf Pilling, was entrusted with the job of putting in working order more than 30 antique railway clocks for the British Transport Commission museum at Clapham, London.

Wilf Pilling and Chargehand Henry Glyn are the men responsible for visiting stations to repair the large clocks that are so well-known to staff and travellers. Although they consider all jobs are much about the same, Wilf said: "A tricky job was dismantling the station clock at Stafford. With an eight-foot pendulum and gear weighing a hundredweight it took us a day to finish it."

On the visit of the *Magazine* Henry was working inside, repairing watches. Asked the main troubles he replied: "Broken balance staffs, generally caused through careless usage. With proper care no watch should require attention for at least 18 months after it leaves here."

Another watch expert is Arthur Taylor, with 11 years' service, who told us that each repairer is responsible for the complete overhaul and cleaning of a watch. Arthur is able to strip down a watch completely and diagnose the trouble in 15 minutes.

Newest member of the shop is Sid Bird, whose burly looks well fit him for his hobby of bass player in a local brass band, entertaining the football crowds at the United and City grounds in Manchester.

When all clocks and watches have been cleaned and repaired they are subjected to a 48-hour test by Harry West. Finally, they are passed to the Stores Issuer Johnny Mulholland – and back they go, in full working order, to the senders.

Above: Johnny Mulholland packs the pendulum of a repaired wall clock as others look down.

Below: Henry Glynn fixes the balance staff.

Opposite: British Railways' Western Region clock repair shop at Reading, 1948–50. Hung over the workers are several cased clocks; an array of tools can be seen on the work benches.

Above: British Railways' London Midland Region Clock and Watch Repair Shop, Manchester, opened 1894 and seen here in 1962.

Railway timekeepers and modernity

Helsinki, Finland, 1919.

The emergence of modern architectural designs in the early twentieth century made it possible to rethink the railway clocktower as a sculptural form as well as a functional landmark.[4] Good examples of clocks integrated with modern railway buildings include Barrow Central, England (British Railways London Midland Region architects, 1958–9), Brest, France (Urbain Cassan, 1936–7), Buffalo Central Terminal, USA (Fellheimer & Wagner, 1927–29), Chichester, England (British Railways Southern Region architects, 1957–61), Cincinnati Union Terminal, USA (Fellheimer & Wagner, 1933), Den Helder, Netherlands (Joost van der Grinten, 1959–61), Dundee Tay Bridge, Scotland (British Railways Scottish Region architects, about 1960), Eindhoven, Netherlands (Koenrad van der Gaast, 1956), Florence, Italy (Gruppo Toscano, 1932–4), Folkestone Central, England (British Railways Southern Region architects, 1962), Helsinki Central, Finland (Eliel Saarinen, 1919), Le Havre Gare de la Ville, France (Henri Pacon, 1930–33), Los Angeles Union Passenger Terminal (Donald and John Parkinson, 1934–9), Richmond, England (Southern Railway architects' department under J R Scott, 1937), Saint Petersburg Finland Station, Russia (Nikolay Baranov, 1960), Santa Maria Novella, Florence, Italy (Gruppo Toscano, 1934–6); Surbiton, England (Southern Railway architects' department under J R Scott, 1937), Tampere Central, Finland (Eero Seppälä and Otto Flodin, 1933–8), and Venlo, Netherlands (Koenrad van der Gaast, 1958).

Folkestone Central, England, 1962.

Buffalo Central, USA, 1927–9.

Le Havre, France, 1933.

Santa Maria Novella, Florence, Italy, 1934–6.

2420_ BREST_ La Tour de l'Horloge
Nouvelle gare (arch URBAIN CASSAN, L. BRASSEUR scul.

Brest, France, 1936–7.

Tampere, Finland, 1933–8.

Eindhoven, Netherlands, 1956.

Venlo, Netherlands, 1958.

Den Helder, Netherlands, 1959–61.

Above: Barrow Central, England, 1958–9.　　　　　　　　　　**Opposite**: Chichester, England, 1957–61.

Dundee Tay Bridge, Scotland, about 1960.

There are several interesting clock designs on the London Underground system at Bethnal Green, Oakwood, Redbridge, Ruislip Manor, and Southgate, designed by architects Charles Holden, Stanley Heaps and colleagues during 1932–38.

Clockwise from top left: Bethnal Green, designed 1938, opened 1946; Southgate, 1933; Ruislip Manor, 1938; Oakwood, 1933.

Top and above: dial and mechanism of a Gent's primary clock, which generates electrical impulses to control multiple secondary dial clocks.

Above: publicity for Gent's secondary impulse dial clocks, early 1960s.

Above: A Gent's Pul-syn-etic secondary dial clock at Queen's Park, London, 1965.

By the 1840s awareness of how electromagnetic principles could be used in the measurement and communication began to produce practical applications. Further innovation enabled many secondary 'impulse dials' to be connected by wires to a single primary regulating mechanism, so that an exact and identical time was available across different parts of a building or around a network. British Railways and other organisations used the Synchronome (Everett, Edgcumbe & Company, London), Pul-syn-etic (Gent of Leicester), and systems from the early twentieth century until the development of digital systems and individual small quartz-based clock movements.

Above left: Birmingham New Street, England, 1967–8;
Left: Netherfield and Colwick, England, 1962;
Above: Harlow New Town, England, 1959–60.

Opposite above: Manchester Oxford Road, England, 1959–60;
Opposite below: Runcorn, England, about 1960.

Top: Plymouth, England, 1966;
Above: Potters Bar, England, 1955;
Right: Folkestone Central, England, 1962.

Opposite: St Helens, Shaw Street, England, 1961.

Vol. 13 No. 6 June 1962

British Railways **Magazine** 5d

Southern Region **Insurance Edition**

Just the job

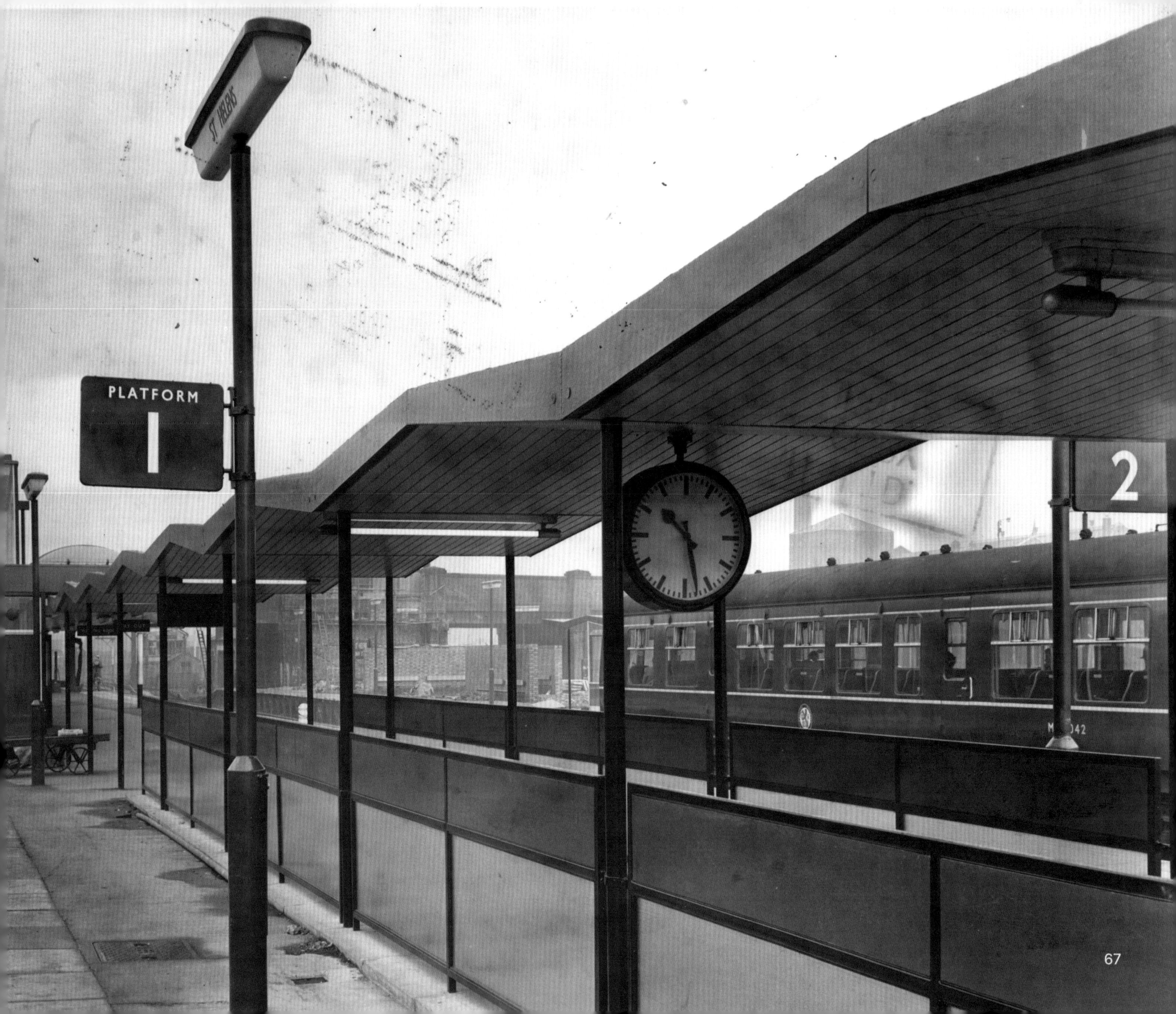
ST HELENS
PLATFORM
1
2

Clocks were integrated into the designs of new British railway stations and other facilities built during the 1930s–60s.

The platform clock must compete visually with the equipment and advertising, signs and other elements of railway operation. It must be visible; it should perhaps give an audible indication of the time; it must be easy to install and maintain or repair.

Above: Nuneaton, England, 1988;
Left: Cardiff, Wales, 1970s.

Swindon, England, 1990s.

Liverpool Street, London, England, 1960s.

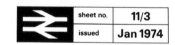

1   **Face**   Standard BR clock face for station concourses and similar situations.

Face of clock white (or silver anodised). Dial markings, hour and minute hands black. Second hand red.

Full size bromide prints of dial markings (and hands) suitable for reproduction by screen printing are available from the Director of Industrial Design, BRB.

Please state whether for
(a)   white (or aluminium) face
(b)   internally illuminated translucent face
(c)   white on black face.

2   **Movement**   Hour and minute hands driven by half-minute impulse movement. Sweep second hand driven by synchronous AC movement, synchronised with minute hand at each minute.

3   **Sizes**   Recommended sizes 250mm, 300mm, 450mm, and 600mm diameter.

Opposite: Quartz crystal oscillators (first made accurate by W A Marrison, 1929), have been incorporated into transistor and circuit micro-circuitry to produce small, cheap movements powering individual clocks. British Rail created a standard clock face design around 1973, without numerals, and with different sizes of baton mark to indicate the hours and minutes. Timekeepers with the dial design were installed across the British Rail system.

Left above: Chester, England, 1991;
Left below: Dundee, Scotland, 1988.

From 1954 Gino Valle, working also with John Myer, created clocks for Italian organisation *Solari* using the electro-mechanical 'flip' system. The classic form of this timepiece is the *Cifra 3*. Britain's railways installed *Solari* devices in stations constructed or rebuilt in the 1960s and 1970s, including London Euston (**opposite**), Birmingham New Street, and London Kings Cross (**above**).

73

To improve management and efficiency British Rail was divided into different sectors from 1982. The Network SouthEast sector formed in 1986 used an electro-mechanical clock with numerals mimicking the appearance of LCD digits, as the standard timekeeping device across its network from East Anglia to the West of England, and into the Midlands.

After mechanical clock movements, transistors, micro-circuitry, and 'atomic' clocks have subsequently provided a more easily maintained method of clock regulation. Precision in timekeeping means we can know that the average solar day comprises 86,400 seconds, and that in every hour there are 3,600 seconds. Accurate time

Clockwise from top left: Hedge End, England, 1990; East Croydon, England, 1992; London King's Cross, England, 2022.

Left: Former Eurostar terminus at Waterloo featuring dial-face clock.

Above: Eurostar timetable featuring the Waterloo terminus clock.

can now be shared around the planet and deep into space.

The provision of large-scale information indicators of the *Solari* type, supplemented and superseded by television monitors (Video Announcement Systems), liquid crystal displays (LCD), and now LED displays, required the development of centralised computer networks to manage the time and the train information being presented on screen. Links into the train signalling equipment help to ensure the information presented to passengers is accurate, or 'real time'. Many of these large and monolithic indicators are supplemented by smaller units located near to groups of platforms.

The *Eurostar* London-Paris link offers examples of prominent dial-face timekeepers at London Waterloo (now demolished), and in the TGV environment. Most recently

Network Rail included a prototype for a standard railway clock in the design of the modular station building at Corby, (2009), and in the proposals for a new modular Network Rail station by *7N Architects*.

Live updates through global positioning systems and other data feeds combine and compare the real time and the timetable, so we know where the train is actually positioned, as well as where it should be located. In this context of massive data flows the railway clock has become a symbol of precise, organised time. It is no longer indispensable, but it is an important, indeed fundamental icon of rail transport.

The value of the clock in communicating the public 'face' and brand image of railway networks has ensured its presence in new projects of the last half-century.

Above: Sketch of the proposed
Greenhithe station, 2008,
with illustration of potential
new railway clock.

Right: Prototype for a clock to
complement Network Rail's modular
stations, with inspiration from European
railway clock styling, 2009.

Clockwise from top left: digital time displays at Andover, 2022; Ipswich, 2021; Birmingham New Street, 2022; Maidenhead, 2022.

Looking beyond:
product design for timekeeping

Swiss railway clock, St Niklaus, Switzerland, 1962.

International product design has contributed to the face and form of the railway timekeeper and other modern timepieces. The Swiss Federal Railways (SBB) clock first designed by Hans Hilfiker in 1944 is now one of the most well-known transport clocks, and is also sold as a wristwatch manufactured by *Mondaine*. Several excellent examples of timepiece design for the railway clock (Bahnhofsuhr) and for commercial or domestic use have been produced in Germany.

Telefonbau und Normalzeit, *Gerätewerk Leipzig*, and members of the *Rundfunk- und Fernmelde-Technik* manufacturing combine, all made clocks for railway and public or industrial use. The Czech *Electrocas Pragotron* company continues to produce clocks for transport, industrial, and domestic applications. In Sweden *Westerstrand* manufactured railway timekeepers for domestic use and export: they were installed at refurbished London Underground stations during the 1980s.

Also on the London Underground, *Design Research Unit* had worked with London Transport architects to integrate timekeepers with dial faces into the stainless steel platform end wall units of Victoria line stations (opened 1968–72).

European clocks for transport
and industrial contexts:

Clockwise from top left:
Deutsche Bahn (German Railways); Pragotron
(Czech Republic); DSB (Danish State Railways);
Statens Järnvägar (Swedish State Railways).

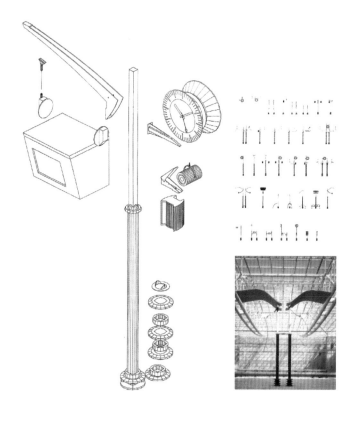

Clock dial and passenger information system designed by Christian Descamps for the French SNCF TGV *Atlantique* system (opened 1989–90) and now made and marketed by bodet-time.com.

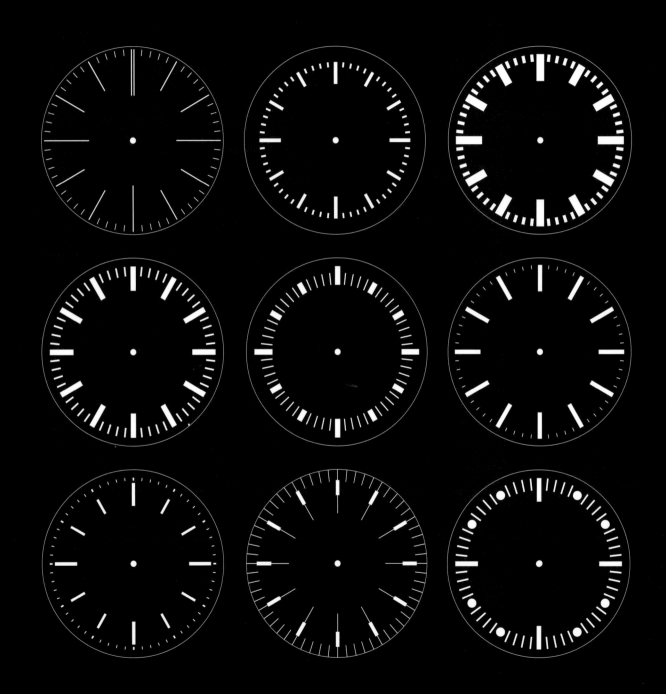

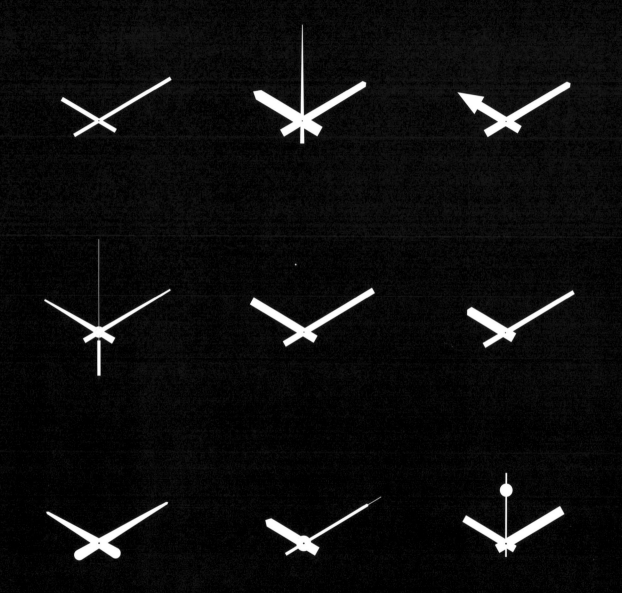

Cergy, north-west of Paris, France, developed as a new town from 1968. One concept for the town planning features a 'Major Axis' themed around astronomy and time, which gives a visual link between the centre of Cergy and the City of Paris. Aligned almost due north of the 'Major Axis' is the Gare de Cergy Saint-Christophe, designed by P.O. Commarteau, 1985. Taking up the theme of time, the concourse through the station passes under a barrel vault roof whose end screens are clocks of 10 metres diameter designed by architects Martine and Philippe Deslandes and watchmaker Huchez.

Four video stills of the Maarten Baas clock at Schiphol airport, Amsterdam, the Netherlands, in 2016. From the 'Real Time' series of clocks, this installation shows a worker manually painting the hands which indicate the time, and then erasing the hands before repeating the actions.

Aspects of timepiece design relevant to the appearance of clocks – brand, consistency and variety, status, precision, miniaturisation, information presented, and decoration – are discovered by looking at clocks and wristwatches designed for non-rail contexts.

AEG, a pioneer of industrial design, has made several exemplary small clocks, including models by Peter Behrens (from around 1910) and the 'Typ BUT' (about 1970) by Kurt M. Traeg. Max Bill designed clocks for *Junghans* distinguished by their slender index marks and hands. For *Braun*, Dieter Rams and Dietrich Lubs have authored numerous timepieces since the early 1970s. Kenneth Grange 'Mariner' for *Taylor Instrument Companies* (1971); Jasper Morrison for *MUJI* (2006–8) and *Punkt.* (2011); Sebastian Wrong's 'Font Clock' for *Established & Sons* (2007) are also of interest.

Opposite: **clockwise from top left**: mantel clock by Hermann Esch for Junghans, Germany, about 1929; wall clock by Max Bill for Junghans, about 1957; *Mariner* by Kenneth Grange for Taylor Instruments, USA, 1971 (illustration by Björn Altmann).

This page: **clockwise from bottom left**: *Typ BUQ*, AEG, Germany, about 1970; *Typ BUT* by Kurt M. Traeg for AEG, about 1970; *Font Clock* by Sebastian Wrong for Established & Sons, 2007. *The Font Clock is a reinvented timepiece which is at once both instantly recognisable and similarly curious. Its form and function are familiar, yet the use of twelve different typefaces gives the design a contemporary feel.*

For sophisticated modern dials displaying a rich array of information in many formats several wristwatch manufacturers' products are of interest, including *Apple, Breitling, Bulova, Cartier, Casio, Chanel, Chopard, EBEL, EMC, Hamilton, Lipp, Longines, Mr Jones, Newgate, Omega, Patek Philippe, Rolex, Seiko, Storm, Swatch ®, TAG Heuer, Tudor*, and others. These wearable timepieces are clues to the future appearance of the railway timekeeper, a face and icon of efficient, safe, environmentally positive public transport.

Opposite: **upper row left to right**: Mondaine *Classic Swiss Watch*; *Cyclops*, Mr Jones, England, 2009; *A Perfectly Useless Afternoon*, Mr Jones, England, 2019.

Opposite: **lower row left to right**: *Big Bold Jellyfish*, *Random Ghost Again* and *Nature Blur*, all by Swatch®, Switzerland.

This page: **clockwise from top left**: *Omega Speedmaster*, Switzerland, first developed 1957 and later certified by NASA for use in space (illustration by Björn Altmann); Max Bill *Chronoscope* for Junghans, Germany, 1961 (illustration by Björn Altmann); *Chromachron* by Tian Harlan, Germany, 1973–8.

Body, face, and hands: anatomy of the clock

If you take a clock apart, you will not discover anything about time, but you will become intimate with the mechanisms devised to measure and communicate regular intervals of duration. Parts of analogue clocks were named after the human body. They have 'faces' (more accurately called *dials*) and 'hands'. In analogue clock faces mechanical movement is displayed as movement through space - around the circle of the face through the day-night cycle. The usual form of displaying the time comprised a dial or dials, a form of visual display once ubiquitous in powered vehicles and industry. The dial must of of an appropriate size to be legible in the position it will be displayed. The relative dimensions of fixed marks on the dial, and the indicator hands which will point to these marks, must be balanced to be effective. A clock dial must be precise in its indication of time to be useful, and this can be accomplished by clarity in the face design or definition of the hands.

The cased railway clock dial was typically *written* – this is the term for adding painted marks to the painted or enamelled plain circular or square face – marked with twelve Roman numerals for the hours, and with the fourth hour shown as 'IIII' rather than 'IV' to give visual balance opposite 'VIII' on the dial. If the band marked with hours and minutes has a hollow centre, it is called a *chapter-ring*. If a band subdivided into sixty segments is present outside the numerals, it is a *minute* band. In the larger clocks dials were commonly fabricated from metal, with opaque glass if they were to be illuminated. Some of the most beautiful clocks have dials of metal engraved with intricate decorative numerals, enhanced by further engraving and frosting of the surface (matting). Cheaper dials are fabricated from pressed, stove-enamelled, or screen-

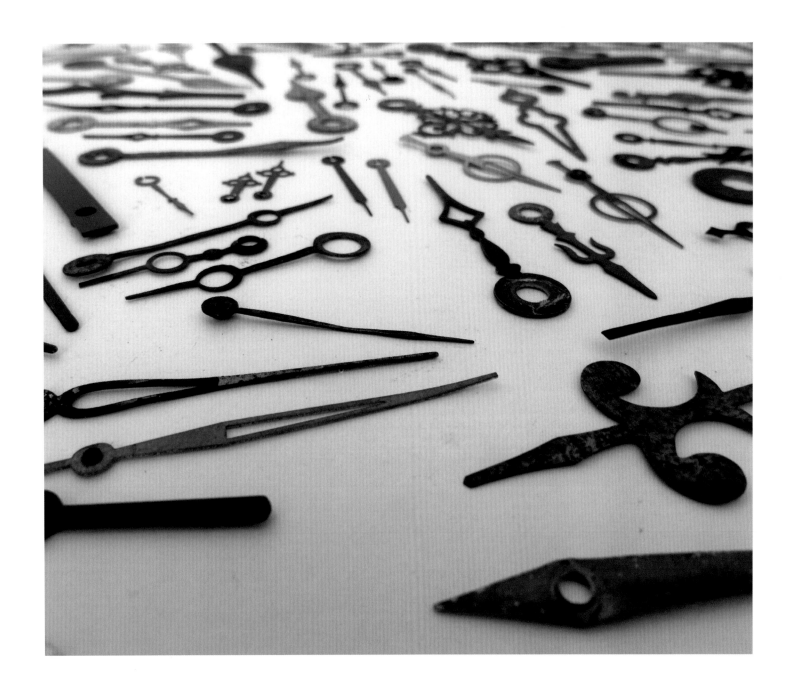

printed metal. By the early twentieth century numbers superseded roman numerals for new clock dials, whilst the older faces continued in use until replaced by new equipment. Red numbers were added to dials from the mid-twentieth century to create twenty-four-hour clocks. Dials may be flat, convex, or concave.

Most commonly the hands make a rotational traverse of the face. When young, before we discover the number of degrees in a circle, we are taught to recognise the patterns of angles which are the positions of the clock hands, and so learn to read the time. This recognition is so embedded that clocks can be read without numerals on their faces. Where there are different types of visual accessibility, the clock must communicate through sound or other means.

In digital displays the character shapes are partly defined by the display components: light-emitting diodes, liquid crystals, or plasma display panels.

Two hands point to the hour and to the minute: conventionally the hour hand would be shorter to avoid obscuring the hour numeral and would have a terminal shaped like the spade symbol on a playing card. The minute hand would be longer and with less decoration. The hands are cut (fretted) or stamped from metal sheet, and then heat-treated (blued) to prevent discolouration or oxidisation. Painted or plastic hands are a cheaper alternative. On large clocks the hands would include casted in metal, or formed by shaping and folding of sheet metal to give structural support to the hands. The black or red centre-seconds sweep hand usefully conveys accuracy and positive continuous movement of the network. With digital equipment, the dial no longer needs to reflect the shape of the mechanism.

As modernity influenced clock designers and manufacturers, graphic design and typography became increasingly important factors for styling dials to give maximum readability of the time. With the reduction of decoration, proportion in overall size and the relationship of sizes of arms and index marks also becomes more critical. The selection of a suitable typeface for the dial requires careful work to ensure that the numerals are legible and in proportion to the size of the dial or display. A dial with 'Roman' numerals requires only three different characters – I, V, and X – to mark the hours. A dial with 'Arabic' numerals required ten different characters. The quantity of numerals – I-XII, 1–24, 1–12, 3, 6, 9, 12, or 12 alone – also becomes a factor. Between the numerals rectangular, circular, or lozenge-shaped symbols called *indexes* or *batons*, *graduations*, *register marks* or *minute marks* are subdivisions representing minutes. Again, visibility is an important feature if these marks are to be useful.

If the hours are indicated without numerals, their position is shown by *batons* or *chaplets*. Without the additional information of numerals, the sizes, proportions and positions of these marks becomes more important. Too fine and they will not be seen; too thick and they become inaccurate.

In digital displays the character shapes are partly defined by the display components: light-emitting diodes, liquid crystals, or plasma display panels.

Thinking about railway timekeepers

Designers, architects, and engineers ask many questions when considering the placing of timekeepers in the railway environment

Location
Where do we look for the time?
Up, down? How high? How low?

Will the clock be a landmark, meeting place, point of interest?

Can the clock be integrated with existing architecture and space?
Is the clock suitable for the Network Rail modular station?

Is there one big clock, or many small clocks?

Is the design, or a version of the design, appropriate for these spaces: station approaches, bus stop or bus station, car park, taxi rank, concourse, ticket office, ticket machines, train arrival and departure indicator, ticket barriers, platforms, waiting rooms, cafés, shops, bars, catering and retail units, toilets, staff offices, staff rest rooms?

Form
Does the design meet all or most accessibility requirements?
Is the design consistent *and* adaptable?

What is the case/enclosure shape: round because the dial is round and time is represented as cycles, or square/rectangular to appear modern, mechanical or digital?

How about materials and decoration: luxury or utility?

Will colour be used to enhance the display or communicate geographical location?

Will the location name feature in the display?

Users
How are commuters/tourists/visitors/shoppers/ operating staff/ rail workers/passers-by informed by the clock?
Is the clock displayed for the passenger, or to show that the railway knows time is important?

How does the clock communicate to differently abled visitors?

Display
Is the time display analogue, digital, or a hybrid of indications?
Does the clock use light, sound, animation, aroma, vibration?

What information will be displayed: hours, minutes, seconds, date, moon phase, news bulletins, meteorological conditions, alarm notifications, messages to persons at the station?

Does the 'face' include the rail operator brand symbol and colour(s) to indicate a reliable national brand?

Is the display area efficient?
Are there multiple dials, or dials within dials, or displays within dials?

Is/are the dial/dials inspired or influenced by scientific equipment, motor car/automobile or aviation instrumentation?

Are numbers to indicate the hours, or other types of mark used?

Will there be moving hands or changing numerals?

Are the components visible, as in a 'skeleton' clock?

What powers the clock: is it the time signal, electrical or electronic pulse, digital, wind, water, sun, passenger footfall?

What indication is there of this power source: light, movement, sound, animation? Is the timepiece carbon zero in manufacture, installation, and operation?

Are the components and modules easy to maintain and replace?

Clock-words (a glossary)

Arbor
The shaft on which elements of a clockwork mechanism are mounted.

Analogue
A display in which the time is indicated by rotating parts.

Arch dial
An analogue clock face with a curved top margin featuring a further part dial.

Automaton
An animated figure moved by a (usually) hidden mechanism.

Balance
Parts of a clock work devised to improve the accuracy of the timekeeping.

Beat
As with the human heart, the number of identical regulating movements in a fixed period of time. A measured count of clock 'ticks' is a beat.

Bezel
Typically a metal ring securing the clear cover of the dial to the casing.

Centre seconds
The hand indicating seconds on a clock dial; also called a sweep hand.

Chapter ring
A circular shape marked with hours and minutes.

Chime
The sound(s) made by the clock to indicate points in time. Other sounds are 'ring', 'tick-tock', and 'ting-tang'.

Cresting
Decorative form and details made for the top portion of a clock case.

Dial and dial-plate
A rectangular, square, or round surface fitted in front of the clock mechanism and marked with hours, minutes, and other information including, for example, the brand of the organisation, the name of the clock maker. Additional details of the dial may be provided to display world time, day, date, phases of the sun and moon, the current astrological sign, or meteorological conditions.

Digital
A display of the time in numerals, generally arranged horizontally, instead of on a dial.

Equation of time
Time derived from a sundial (where the hours are of unequal lengths) compared with time indicated by a clock, as a difference in figures. A helio-chronometer uses the sun to produce the same time reading as a mechanical clock.

Escapement
The regulating mechanism of a mechanical clock, arranged to control the power supplied to the clockwork, and consequently the speed of the clock count.

Foliot
A regulating mechanism used in early timekeeping clock works.

Gnomon (or style)
The fixed vertical element of a sundial that casts a shadow.

Going train
A series of toothed wheels which carry mechanical power supplied to the clock through to the escapement mechanism.

Hood
Case containing the mechanism and dial.

Impulse
A mechanical, electrical, or electronic 'push' to maintain the oscillation of some clocks or clock parts.

Index mark
One of several names used for a line stroke on a clock dial to show the position of an hour and/or a minute.

LCD, LED
Liquid Crystal Display; light-emitting diode.

Lenticle
Transparent panel revealing part of the clock mechanism.

Minute band
A marking of two parallel rings placed one inside the other, and typically outside the ring of numerals, subdivided to indicate minutes around the dial.

Motion work
The wheels arranged after the escapement to rotate the hour, minute, and second hands at their different speeds.

Movement
The complete mechanism of an analogue, electromagnetic, or geared quartz clock.

Orrery
The movements of the planets represented by a mechanical device, often using clock work.

Pendulum
A swinging element used as part of the regulating mechanism in some clocks.

Sideral time
Time measured by the rotation of the earth.

Signature
Marking on the dial giving the name of the clockmaker. This may be painted, engraved, or enamelled.

Skeleton dial
A clock face with parts of the dial removed to reveal portions of the mechanism. Clocks cased more or less fully in translucent materials are called 'skeleton clocks'.

Solar time
The indication of time given by a sundial.

Spandrel
Decorative elements applied to the corners of a clock face outside the circular dial.

Sweep hand
The hand which rotates continuously to indicate seconds.

Turret clock
A display of time usually mounted in a tower or in a prominent position on a building.

Resources: books

Any research about railway timepieces will be diminished if reference is not made to Ian Lyman's book **Railway Clocks** (2004). This is available in PDF form from Mayfield Books: https://www.mayfieldbooks.co.uk/.

Anderson, V., and Fox, G. (1981) **A Pictorial Record of L.M.S. Architecture** (Oxford: Oxford Publishing Co.).

Arup with Network Rail (2019) **Tomorrow's Living Station**. Available at: <https://www.arup.com/perspectives/publications/promotional-materials/section/tomorrows-living-station>.

Baillie, Granville, Ilbert, Courtenay, and Clutton, Cecil. [Eds.] (1982) **Britten's Old Clocks and Watches and their makers: A history of styles in clocks and watches and their mechanisms** [Ninth Edition] (London: Methuen in association with E & F N Spon).

Barman, Christian (1949) **The Things We See: Public Transport** (Harmondsworth: Penguin Books).

Barman, Christian (1950) **An Introduction to Railway Architecture** (London: Art and Technics).

Beresford-Evans, J. (1954) **Form in Engineering Design: The Study of Appearance During Design and Development** (Oxford: Clarendon Press).

Blake, Avril (1984) **Misha Black** (London: The Design Council).

Brindle, Steven. (2004) **Paddington Station: Its history and architecture** (Swindon: English Heritage).

Britten, F. J. (1978) **Britten's Watch & Clock Maker's Handbook Dictionary and Guide** (London: Eyre Methuen).

Brunner, Gisburt, and Pfeiffer-Belli, Christian (1999) **Wristwatches Armbanduhren Montres-bracelets** (Köln: Könemann).

Bruton, Eric (1999) **The History of Clocks and Watches** [first published 1979] (London: Little, Brown and Company).

Centre Georges Pompidou (Beauborg) (1981) **All Stations: A Journey Through 150 Years of Railway History** [first published 1978] (London: Thames and Hudson).

Glancey, Jonathan (1988) **Douglas Scott** (London: The Design Council).

Gorb, Peter [ed.] (1978) **Living by design** (London: Lund Humphries).

Haresnape, Brian (1981) **Design for Steam 1830–1960** (London: Book Club Associates/Ian Allan).

Hernick, James [Ed.] (1996) **Railroad Timekeeping** (Chicago: National Association of Watch & Clock Collectors).

Hill, R. Noel (1949) **Early British Clocks from C. 1600 to C. 1800** (London: The Connoisseur).

Lansley, Alastair, Durant, Stuart, Dyke, Alan, Gambrill, Bernard, and Shelton, Roderick (2008) **The Transformation of St Pancras Station** (London: Laurence King Publishing).

Lawrence, David (2016) **British Rail Designed 1948–97** (London: Ian Allan; Manchester: Crécy Books).

Lawrence, David (2018) **British Rail Architecture 1948–97** (Manchester: Crécy Books).

Lawrence, David, and O'Donovan, Luke (2020) **Hub: Making places for people and trains** (London: Network Rail Infrastructure Limited).

Lyman, Ian P. (1993) **'Railway Clocks' in British Railway Journal**, number 48, Autumn, pp. 363–72.

Lyman, Ian P. (2004) **Railway Clocks** (Ashbourne: Mayfield Books).

Maison du Tourisme et du Patrimonie (undated) **Decouvrez Cergy Naturellement: Parcours architecture quartier Axe Majeur-Horloge** (Cergy: Maison du Tourisme et du Patrimonie).

Meeks, Carroll (1978) **The Railroad Station: An Architectural History** [first published 1956] (Secaucus, New Jersey: Castle Books).

Network Rail (2021) **Our Principles of Good Design**. Available at: <https://www.networkrail.co.uk/wp-content/uploads/2021/06/NR_Our-Principles-of-Good-Design.pdf>.

Network Rail Station (2021) **Station Design Guidance Design Manual** NR/GN/CIV/100/02. Available at: <https://www.networkrail.co.uk/wp-content/uploads/2021/06/NR_GN_CIV_100_02_Station-Design.pdf>.

Network Rail Design Guidance Manuals. Available at: <https://www.networkrail.co.uk/industry-and-commercial/supply-chain/existing-suppliers/buildings-and-architecture-design-guidance/>.

Rooney, David (2021) **About Time: A History of Civilization in Twelve Clocks** (London: Viking).

Rose, Ronald (1988) **English Dial Clocks** [revised edition] (Woodbridge: Antique Collectors' Club).

Schivelbusch, Wolfgang [trans. Anselm Hollo] (1980) **The Railway Journey: Trains and Travel in the 19th Century** [first published 1978] (Oxford: Basil Blackwell).

Sturgis, Alexander (2000) **Telling Time** (London: National Gallery).

Tufte, Edward (1990) **Envisioning Information** (Cheshire, Connecticut: Graphics Press).

Tufte, Edward (2001) **The Visual Display of Quantitative Information: Second edition** [first published 1983] (Cheshire, Connecticut: Graphics Press).

Ullyett, Kenneth (1968) **In Quest of Clocks** [first published 1950] (London: Spring Books).

Ward, F. (1972) **Clocks and Watches: 2: Spring-driven** (London: Her Majesty's Stationery Office).

White, Jeremy [ed.] (2022) **Wired Time** [a supplement to WIRED magazine, January–February 2022] (London: the Condé Nast Publications).

Resources: world wide web

Bjoern Altmann watch faces: www.bjoernaltmann.com/work/watch-faces-b82hf. Find Bjoern Altmann on Instagram and Etsy.

Bodet Time PROFIL TGV clock: www.bodet-time.com/clocks/tgv-clocks.html.

British Museum: www.britishmuseum.org/collection/galleries/clocks-and-watches.

British Rail Corporate Identity: doublearrow.co.uk/home.htm.

British Railway Clocks: railwayclocks.net.

Buffalo Central Terminal: buffalocentralterminal.org. The Clockmakers' Museum: www.sciencemuseum.org.uk/see-and-do/clockmakers-museum.

Corpus Clock, Cambridge: www.corpus.cam.ac.uk/about/corpus-clock/introduction-corpus-clock.

Huxley Bertram Engineering: https://huxleybertram.com.

Mayfield Books, Specialist Publishers of Quality Horological Books: www.mayfieldbooks.co.uk.

Museum of Timekeeping: www.museumoftimekeeping.org.uk.

National Maritime Museum: www.rmg.co.uk.

Royal Observatory Greenwich: www.rmg.co.uk.

Telephone Construction & Normal Time [Telefonbau und Normalzeit]: https://www.telefonbau-und-normalzeit.de/TELEFONBAU-NORMALZEIT-Home.

VintageGermanClocks: www.etsy.com/uk/shop/VintageGermanClocks.

Footnotes

1   In correct horological terms, a clock is a time-measuring device which causes a bell to be struck to announce intervals of time such as hours. Other mechanical and digital time measuring devices are called timekeepers. For simplicity this book uses the word *clock* for all time-measuring and outputting equipment.

2   Rose (1988): 13.

3   In 1884 a world standard time – again the time at Greenwich – would be adopted so that global shipping routes could be operated efficiently.

4   Stations built by colonial governments in territories beyond Europe generally followed European design practices.

Acknowledgements

7N Architects: Ben Watson; Björn Altmann; Tony Armitage; Bodet Time-Bodet Limited: Simon Tennant; Magdalena Boudová; Violetta Boxill; Burton McCall Ltd – Watches for Mondaine UK: Gemma Hine; Buffalo Central Terminal: buffalocentralterminal.org: Monica Pellegrino Faix and Joe Cascio Photography; Margaret Calvert; Michael Collins; Design Museum: Justin McGuirk, Suzanne Moores; Deutsches Uhrenmuseum, Furtwangen University: Dr. Johannes Graf; Established & Sons: Sebastian Wrong, Tamasin Fisher, Aynsley Munsie; Julia Findlater; High Speed 1: Josie Murray; Nick Job: British Rail Corporate Identity at www.doublearrow.co.uk; Leila Lawrence; maartenbaas.com: Iveta; Jonathan McDowell (Matter Architecture); Mayfield Books: John Robey; Museum of Richmond: Laura Irwin, Ffion Lanigan; Mr Jones: Crispin Jones; Museum of Timekeeping; National Association of Watch & Clock Collectors [USA]: Rich Newman, Wayne Pedryc; Network Rail: Frank Anatole, Anthony Dewar; Owen Thomas; Network Rail Corporate Archive; Network Rail Media Centre; Brett Oliver; railwayclocks.net: Simon Turner; RCTS Photo Archive: David Bird; Richmond Information and Reference Library: Fee Campbell; Scott Rigby; Kevin Robertson; David Rooney; Royal Institute of British Architects: James Porter, Hannah Raithby; Julia Davies; Piotr Samulik; Science and Society Picture Library; Swatch ®/The Swatch Group (UK) Limited: Orane Stepczynski; John C Taylor Limited: Dr John C. Taylor OBE, Clare Monaghan, Courtney McClatchey; Robert Thornton; The Transport Treasury; Uhrenmuseum Ehrfurt/Board of Friends of T&N: Marvin Walther; Pavel Vaclavik; Vintage German Clocks: Robert Reinhold; Michael Walton; David Weatherhead; Daniel Weil.

Image Credits